FIRST PAST THE POST ®

Mathematics:
Mental Arithmetic

Standard Format

Book 1

How to use this book to make the most of 11 plus exam preparation

It is important to remember that for 11 plus exams there is no national syllabus, no pass mark and no retake option. It is therefore vitally important that your child is fully primed in order to perform to the best of their ability to give themselves the best possible chance on the day.

Mental arithmetic

This collection of tests is designed to expose your child to a range of question types. The questions provided within this book are intended to develop the fundamental building blocks of mathematics to equip your child with the skills required to sit the numerical reasoning sections of the 11 plus and common entrance exams. The suggested time for each paper is based on data obtained from conventional classroom testing sessions.

Never has it been more useful to learn from mistakes!

Students can improve by as much as 15 percent, not only by focused practice, but also by targeting any weak areas.

How to manage your child's own practice

To get the most up-to-date information, visit our website, www.elevenplusexams.co.uk, the UK's largest online resource for 11 plus, with over 65,000 webpages and a forum administered by a select group of experienced moderators.

About the authors

The Eleven Plus Exams' **First Past the Post®** series has been created by a team of experienced tutors and authors from leading British universities.

Published by University of Buckingham Press

With special thanks to the children who tested our material at the Eleven Plus Exams centre in Harrow.

ISBN: 9781908684462

First Published 2014
Copyright © ElevenPlusExams.co.uk 2014
Revised Edition 2017

About Us

Eleven Plus Exams is the largest website in the UK that specifically prepares children for the 11 plus exams. The website offers a vast amount of information and advice on the 11 plus as well as a moderated online forum, books, downloadable material and online services to enhance your child's chances of success.

The company also provides specialist 11 plus tuition and is a supplier of online services to schools.

Eleven Plus Exams is recognised as a trusted and authoritative source. It has been quoted in numerous national newspapers, including The Telegraph, The Observer, The Daily Mail and The Sunday Telegraph, as well as BBC Radio and national television (BBC1 and Channel 4).

Set up in 2004, the website grew from an initial 20 webpages to more than 65,000 today, and has been visited by millions of parents. The website gives impartial advice on exam preparation and techniques. It is moderated by over 20 experts who provide support for parents both before and after the exams.

Visit our website and see why we are the market's leading one-stop shop for all your 11 plus needs.

- ✓ Comprehensive quality content and advice written by 11 plus experts

- ✓ Eleven Plus Exams online shop supplying a wide range of practice books, e-papers, software and apps

- ✓ Lots of FREE practice papers to download

- ✓ Professional tuition service

- ✓ Short revision courses

- ✓ Year-long 11 plus courses

- ✓ Mock exams tailored to reflect those of the main examining bodies

Other titles in the First Past The Post® Series

11+ Essentials Range of Books

VERBAL REASONING

ISBN	TITLE
9781908684288	Verbal Reasoning: Cloze Tests Book 1
9781908684356	Verbal Reasoning: Cloze Tests Book 2
9781908684639	Verbal Reasoning: Vocabulary Book 1 - Multiple Choice
9781908684783	Verbal Reasoning: Vocabulary Book 2 - Multiple Choice
9781908684844	Verbal Reasoning: Vocabulary Book 3 - Multiple Choice
9781908684646	Verbal Reasoning: Grammar and Spelling Book 1 - Multiple Choice
9781908684790	Verbal Reasoning: Grammar and Spelling Book 2 - Multiple Choice
9781908684868	Verbal Reasoning: Vocabulary in Context Level 1
9781908684875	Verbal Reasoning: Vocabulary in Context Level 2
9781908684882	Verbal Reasoning: Vocabulary in Context Level 3
9781908684889	Verbal Reasoning: Vocabulary in Context Level 4

ENGLISH

ISBN	TITLE
9781908684295	English: Comprehensions Book 1 Classic Literature
9781908684486	English: Comprehensions Book 2 Contemporary Literature
9781908684851	English: Comprehensions Book 3 Non-Fiction

NUMERICAL REASONING

ISBN	TITLE
9781908684431	Numerical Reasoning: Quick-Fire Book 1
9781908684448	Numerical Reasoning: Quick-Fire Book 2
9781908684653	Numerical Reasoning: Quick-Fire Book 1 - Multiple Choice
9781908684752	Numerical Reasoning: Quick-Fire Book 2 - Multiple Choice
9781908684301	Numerical Reasoning: Multi-Part Book 1
9781908684363	Numerical Reasoning: Multi-Part Book 2
9781908684769	Numerical Reasoning: Multi-Part Book 1 - Multiple Choice
9781908684776	Numerical Reasoning: Multi-Part Book 2 - Multiple Choice

MATHEMATICS

ISBN	TITLE
9781908684462	Maths: Mental Arithmetic Book 1
9781908684806	Maths: Worded Problems Book 1
9781908684936	Maths: Worded Problems Book 2
9781908684493	Maths Dictionary Plus

NON-VERBAL REASONING

ISBN	TITLE
9781908684318	3D Non-Verbal Reasoning Book 1
9781908684479	3D Non-Verbal Reasoning Book 2

PUZZLES

ISBN	TITLE
9781908684905	Puzzles: Maths Crosswords
9781908684912	Puzzles: Vocabulary

Test Paper Packs

ISBN	TITLE
9781908684103	English Practice Papers - Multiple Choice Pack 1
9781908684127	Verbal Reasoning Practice Papers - Multiple Choice Pack 1
9781908684134	Non-Verbal Reasoning Practice Papers - Multiple Choice Pack 1
9781908684110	Mathematics Practice Papers - Multiple Choice Pack 1

Contents

This workbook comprises 20 tests, made up of 30 short questions each. Each test should take 10 minutes to complete.

Once each test has been completed and marked using the answers at the back, you can use our 11+ Peer Compare System™ to anonymously compare your child's performance to peers who have completed the same test(s). Register at http://peercompare.elevenplusexams.co.uk and activate the access code printed on the front inside cover of this book.

Instructions

Write your answers on the answer lines provided as shown below:

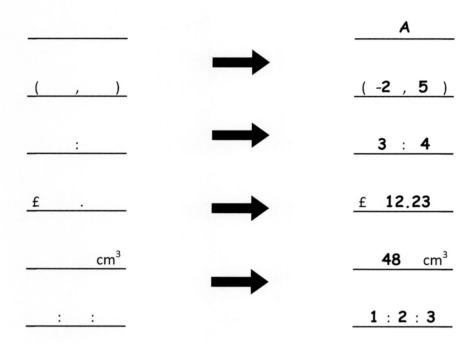

In some of the questions, you are given a table with empty spaces in which to write your answers. Fill in the empty spaces in the tables as shown below:

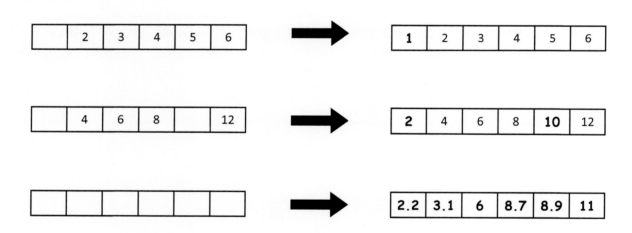

FIRST PAST THE POST®

Tests 1 - 20

Read the following instructions carefully:

1. You have 10 minutes to complete each test of 30 questions.

2. Work as quickly and as carefully as you can.

3. You can use the available space around the questions to do any working. However, only write your final answer on the answer line.

4. To change an answer, rub out your original answer completely and then write down your new answer.

5. If you cannot answer a question, go on to the next question.

6. When you have completed a paper, use the time remaining to go back to any questions you have missed out and check your answers.

7. Calculators, protractors and any other mathematical instruments must not be used.

Once each test has been completed and marked using the answers at the back, you can use our 11+ Peer Compare System™ to anonymously compare your child's performance to peers who have completed the same test(s). Register at http://peercompare.elevenplusexams.co.uk and activate the access code printed on the front inside cover of this book.

Total
/30

1. What is the value of x?

    156 ——→ | + 134 | ——→ x

    _____

2. Round 56.6572 to the nearest tenth.

    _____

3. What is $^3/_5$ of 570ml?

    _____ ml

4. Calculate 62.4 divided by 6.

    _____

5. What is the value of x?

    _____ °

6. Calculate 7 multiplied by 29.

    _____

7. Simplify $^{42}/_{52}$.

    _____

8. Fill in the spaces below so that the pattern stays the same.

    | 3 | 18 | 9 | 54 | 27 | | |

9. Ravi's scores for six tests are 78%, 90%, 85%, 85%, 77% and 87%. What is his modal score?

    _____ %

10. Express 0.82 as a fraction in its simplest form.

    _____

11. The sign below shows the price of hot dogs. What is the total cost of six large and two small hotdogs?

    £ _____ . ___

12. Express $^{81}/_{90}$ as a percentage.

    _____ %

13. How many sides does this shape have?

    _____

14. A bag contains five balls, three of which are yellow. What is the probability of picking a yellow ball from the bag? Give your answer as a fraction.

    _____

15. How many cubes of a volume of 2cm^3 can you cut out from this clay cube?

    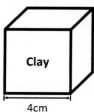

    Clay

    4cm

    _____

16. How many faces does a square pyramid have?

_____

17. What is the area of this isosceles triangle?

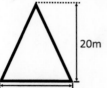

_____ m²

18. What is the difference between the fourth and the eleventh square numbers?

_____

19. $5x + 3 = 18$. What is the value of x?

_____

20. What is the value of x?

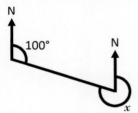

_____ °

21. How many lines of symmetry does a parallelogram have?

_____

22. The perimeter of this square is 24cm. What is the area of the shaded region?

_____ cm²

23. The time now is 08:16. What was the time 5 ¹/₂ hours ago? Give your answer in 24-hour clock format.

_____ :

24. Which of these shapes is an enlargement of shape A?

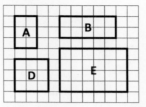

_____

25. Calculate 25 × 9 + 133.

_____

26. What is the volume of a cube with sides of 5cm in length?

_____ cm³

27. What is the ratio of the shaded to unshaded fractions of this circle in its simplest form?

_____ :

28. What is the lowest common multiple (LCM) of the numbers 5, 3 and 9?

_____

29. What is the smallest angle between two perpendicular lines?

_____ °

30. Look at the diagram below. How much does a half-gallon of milk weigh?

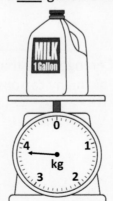

_____ kg

1. What is the ratio 56:72 in its simplest form?

_____ :_____

2. Round 98,398 to the nearest thousand.

_____

3. Calculate 789 + 572.

_____

4. Calculate 10.4 divided by 0.8.

_____

5. Reyvanth buys two footballs which cost £3.20 each with a £20 note. How much change does he receive?

£_____._____

6. James buys 19 boxes of orange juice that hold 25 cartons each. How many cartons does he have in total?

_____

7. Calculate $^7/_{11} \times {}^2/_9$.

_____

8. What is the 9th term in the following sequence: 2, 4, 8, 16, 32, ...?

_____

9. What is the bearing of A from B?

_____ °

10. What is the mean of the following set of numbers: 5, 10, 15, 30, 20?

_____

11. Terry scores 13 out of 25 in his English test. What is his score expressed as a decimal?

_____

12. Express the time on this digital clock in 12-hour clock format.

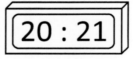

_____

13. What is 55% of £250?

£_____._____

14. Calculate $4^2 + (10 - 5)$.

_____

15. The volume of this prism is 40cm³. What is the area of one of its hexagonal faces?

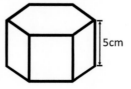

_____ cm²

16. Which of the arrows A, B, C or D shows the best position on the probability line for the event of choosing the letter B from the letters of the word BUBBLE?

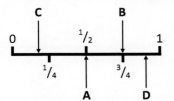

_____

17. Look at the net of a 3D shape below. How many edges does the 3D shape have?

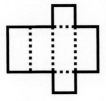

_____

18. Simplify $3x + 5y - 2x + 4y$.

_____

19. What is the cube number that is more than 300 but less than 500?

_____

20. The total area of this shape is 50cm². What is the value of $h$cm?

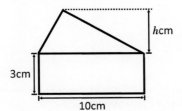

_____ cm

21. How many lines of symmetry does a scalene triangle have?

_____

22. What are the coordinates of point P (3, -5) after a reflection in the x-axis?

(_____ , _____)

23. Which of these shapes is a quadrilateral?

_____

24. Express 6.33pm in 24-hour clock format.

_____ : _____

25. What are the prime factors of 20?

_____

26. How many faces does an octahedron have?

_____

27. What is the difference between the largest and smallest angles in an right-angled isosceles triangle?

_____ °

28. The graph below shows the time taken by Grace to walk a distance of 4km. How many minutes does she take to walk 4km?

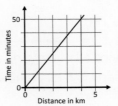

_____ min

29. What is the complementary angle of 24°?

_____ °

30. Look at the pie chart below. Given that 294 items were sold altogether, how many more bananas were sold than apples?

□ bananas □ apples

_____

Test 3

Total
/30

1. What is 30% of 250?

_____

2. How many sides does this shape have?

_____

3. A train leaves London at 09:55 and arrives in Cambridge at 11:05. How long was the journey?

_____ min

4. A school has exactly twice as many girls as boys. Given that there are 576 boys, how many girls are there?

_____

5. How many lines of symmetry does a regular octagon have?

_____

6. Express $^9/_{30}$ as a percentage.

_____ %

7. What is the volume of this cube?

11cm

_____ cm^3

8. Calculate 567 + 234.

_____

9. Round 658.9566 to the nearest hundredth.

_____

10. What is the fifth cube number?

_____

11. Shawn buys six chocolate bars that cost 85p each. How much money does he spend?

£ _____ .

12. Fill in the space below so that the pattern stays the same.

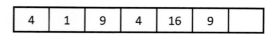

| 4 | 1 | 9 | 4 | 16 | 9 | |

13. How many vertices does this shape have?

_____

14. When the cylinder below is sliced across the middle, parallel to its base, which resulting 2-dimensional shape can be viewed from above?

_____

15. Calculate $1\frac{2}{5} + \frac{7}{15}$. Give your answer as a mixed number.

_____

16. Express 624cm in metres.

_____ m

17. What is the value of x?

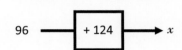

96 ——→ [+ 124] ——→ x

_____

18. $i = 4$ and $j = 2$. Calculate $\frac{16}{i}$ and give your answer in terms of j.

_____

19. What is sixty-seven thousand, five hundred and twenty-two expressed in digits?

_____

20. John flips a fair coin twice consecutively. What is the chance of the coin landing on heads both times? Give your answer as a fraction.

_____

21. What is the mean of the following set of numbers: 5, 6, 8, 1, 15, 7?

_____

22. What is the value of x?

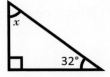

32°

_____ °

23. Given that an equilateral triangle has a perimeter of 54cm, what is the length of each side?

_____ cm

24. 6th June is a Friday. On which day will June 22nd fall in that same year?

_____

25. Jennie and Sonia share this bag of sweets in the ratio 3:2 respectively. How many sweets does Sonia get?

25 sweets

_____

26. Express $7\frac{1}{8}$ as an improper fraction.

_____

27. What is the mode of the following set of numbers: 1, 2, 5, 6, 7, 1, 5, 8, 9, 1?

_____

28. What is the sum of 4,587 and 236?

_____

29. What is the order of rotational symmetry of this shape?

_____

30. Calculate $3 \times 5^2 - 65$.

_____

FIRST PAST THE POST

Test 4

Total
/30

1. What number is 12 more than 6?

_____

2. What is the difference in length between the longest and the shortest of these lines?

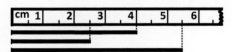

_____ cm

3. What is the ratio of 500 miles to 125 miles in its simplest form?

_____ :

4. Calculate 108 ÷ 6.

_____

5. What is the digit in the ten-thousands column in the number 8,343,674?

_____

6. Teams receive three points for a win (W) and a point for a draw (D). No points are awarded for a loss (L). Which team has the fewest points?

	W	D	L
Team 1	4	2	3
Team 2	2	4	5
Team 3	3	5	2

_____

7. Fill in the spaces below so that the pattern stays the same.

3	6	9		15		

8. Calculate $^9/_7 \div {}^3/_4$. Give your answer as an improper fraction.

_____

9. What is the bearing of B from A?

_____ °

10. The mean of three numbers is 11. Given that two of the numbers are 8 and 15. What is the other number?

_____

11. Five-twelfths of the pupils in a class of 36 support Brimton FC (BFC). How many pupils do not support BFC?

_____

12. What is the volume of this triangular prism?

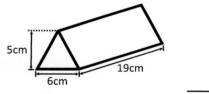

_____ cm³

13. Calculate 50 - 10 ÷ 2 + 55.

_____

14. A calculator costing £15.00 is reduced in price by 40%. How much does it cost now?

£ _____ . _____

15. What is the probability of zero being greater than one? Give your answer as a percentage.

_____ %

16. Calculate 5.67 - 1.76.

_____

17. What is 9°C below the temperature shown on this thermometer?

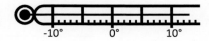

_____ °C

18. $8x - 12 = -5x + 27$. What is the value of x?

_____

19. Calculate $4^2 + 3^3 - 12$.

_____

20. Given that the perimeter of this triangle is 47mm, what is the length of the side AC.

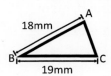

_____ mm

21. Calculate 195 multiplied by 9.

_____

22. Shape ABCD is rotated about the origin in an anticlockwise direction to give shape A'B'C'D'. Through what angle is ABCD rotated?

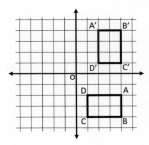

_____ °

23. Express 21:54 in 12-hour clock format.

_____

24. What is the median of the prime factors of 21?

_____

25. The graph shows the time taken by Alex to run a distance of 1km. Estimate the distance he covered in the first 6 minutes to the nearest 100m.

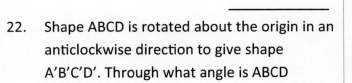

_____ m

26. An interior angle of a trapezium is 100°. What is the sum of the other three angles?

_____ °

27. How many square pyramids do you need to make an octahedron?

_____

28. How many lines of symmetry does this shape have?

_____

29. What is the number of sides of a hexagon cubed?

_____

30. What is the supplementary angle of 134°?

_____ °

FIRST PAST THE POST

Test 5

Total
/30

1. What is the value of x?

354 ——— + 65 ———→ x

_____

2. $5 \times 6 = 300 \div b$. What is the value of b?

_____

3. How many pairs of parallel lines does a regular octagon have?

_____

4. What is the remainder of $457 \div 5$?

_____

5. What is the perimeter of this shape?

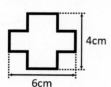

4cm

6cm

_____ cm

6. Express $^{13}/_{65}$ as a percentage.

_____ %

7. What is the difference between 423 and 345?

_____

8. A recipe for cookies uses 24 cups of flour, 8 cups of butter and 6 cups of sugar. What is the ratio of flour to butter to sugar?

_____ : _____ : _____

9. Shape ABC is an equilateral triangle. What is the bearing of A from B?

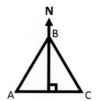

_____ °

10. What is the mode of the following set of numbers: 1, 2, 3, 2, 1, 2, 3, 4, 1, 2, 4?

_____

11. What is the probability of a fair coin landing on heads when it is tossed? Give your answer as a decimal.

_____

12. What is ninety-four thousand, eight hundred and seventy-three expressed in digits?

_____

13. Express $5\,^{3}/_{7}$ as an improper fraction.

_____

14. What is the number shown by the arrow in digits?

789 793

_____

15. Calculate $2 \times 3 + (5 - 1)^2$.

_____

16. $4x + 10y - 2z = w$. Given that $x = 6$, $y = 2$ and $z = 15$, what is the value of w?

_____

17. Fill in the spaces below so that the pattern stays the same.

	162	54	18	6	

18. What are the three square numbers that have a sum of 26?

_____

19. Given that the perimeter of an equilateral triangle is 117mm, what is the length of each side?

_____ mm

20. Which of these shapes has exactly two lines of symmetry?

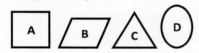

_____

21. What are the coordinates of point T (0, 5) after a clockwise rotation of 90° about the origin?

(_____ , _____)

22. The time now is 13:57. What will the time be 82 minutes later? Give your answer in 24-hour clock format.

_____ : _____

23. Kevin and Songyo each receive £19.50 for their school lunches every week. How much money should they receive collectively over two weeks?

£ _____ . _____

24. The diagram below shows the plan and elevations of a 3D shape made up of smaller cubes. How many smaller cubes are there?

Plan   Front   Side
Elevation   Elevation

_____

25. Express $^1/_9$ as a decimal to 3 decimal places.

_____

26. What is the highest common factor (HCF) of 65, 30 and 45?

_____

27. This graph shows the temperature over 5 days. Find the mean daily temperature.

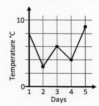

_____ °C

28. How many vertices does a tetrahedron have?

_____

29. It costs £2.80 to travel 10km. How much does it cost to travel 70km at the same rate?

£ _____ . _____

30. This cuboid is made up of smaller cubes of volume 1cm^3. What is the volume of the cuboid?

_____ cm^3

FIRST PAST THE POST

Test 6

Total
/30

1. 6 - a = 0. What is the value of a?

_____

2. Write six tens and two ones as digits.

_____

3. What is the ratio of £2.00 to £3.60 in its simplest form?

_____ : _____

4. Divide 33 by the sum of 0.11 and 0.99.

_____

5. Raman eats six chocolates every day from a box of fifty-four. For how many days will the box last?

_____

6. Calculate 250 multiplied by 11.

_____

7. Shape ABCD is a square. What is the bearing of B from D?

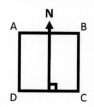

_____ °

8. What is the 54th term given that the nth term of a sequence is as follows: 3(n - 6)?

_____

9. Calculate $^2/_5$ divided by $^3/_4$.

_____

10. What is the value of x?

_____

11. On Sundays Tanvi spends $^3/_8$ of the day sleeping. For how many hours is she awake?

_____ hr

12. What is the mean length of two ribbons that are 8.7m and 3.9m long?

_____ m

13. A jumper costing £15.00 is reduced in price by 45%. How much does it now cost?

£ _____ . _____

14. The heights of five children are 155cm, 146cm, 175cm, 160cm and 152cm. What is the range of their heights?

_____ cm

15. It is afternoon and Divisha has her piano lesson 45 minutes after the time shown on this clock. What time is her lesson? Give your answer in 12-hour clock format.

_____

16. What is the probability of rolling an odd number with a fair die? Give your answer as a fraction.

_____

17. What is the volume of a cuboid which measures 9cm by 2cm by 14cm?

_____ cm^3

18. Look at the diagram below. Given that the perimeters of the square and the equilateral triangle are 40m and 21m respectively, what is the value of xm?

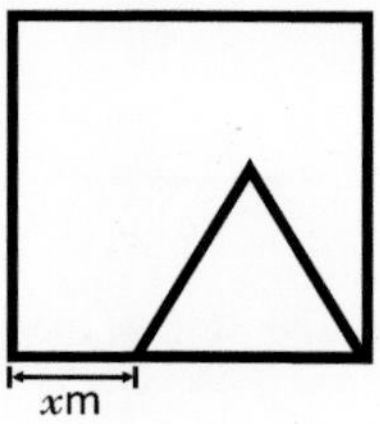

_____ m

19. What is the sum of the first five prime numbers?

_____

20. Kushal has six boxes, each containing x chocolates, and four boxes, each containing y sweets. Write an expression which represents the total number of chocolates and sweets Kushal has.

_____

21. What is the order of rotational symmetry of this shape?

_____

22. What is the exterior angle of a regular polygon with three sides?

_____ °

23. What are the coordinates of point A (-5, 6) after a reflection in the y-axis?

(_____ , _____)

24. The time now is 19:11. What was the time 39 minutes ago? Give your answer in 12-hour clock format.

_____

25. The lengths of the sides of a triangle are in the ratio 7:11:12. Given that the perimeter of the triangle is 90cm, what is the length of the shortest side?

_____ cm

26. List all the factors of 25.

_____

27. The diagram below shows the plan and elevations of a 3D shape made up of smaller cubes. How many smaller cubes are there?

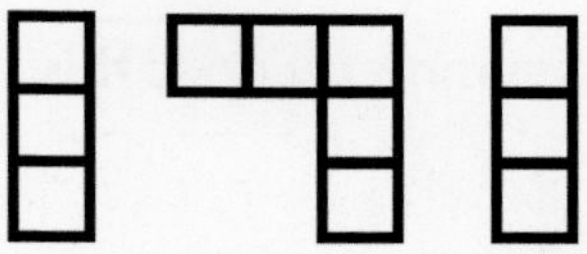

Plan   Front   Side
        Elevation   Elevation

_____

28. Express 0.99 as a fraction.

_____

29. What is the sum of the interior angles of a pentagon?

_____ °

30. How many right angles are there in 270°?

_____

FIRST PAST THE POST

Test 7

```
Total
/30
```

1. What number is triple six?

_____

2. Round 378.398 to the nearest hundred.

_____

3. A recipe for pancakes requires 240g of flour to make 12 pancakes. What quantity of flour is needed to make four pancakes?

_____ g

4. How many lines of symmetry does this shape have?

_____

5. Calculate 6543 - 1850.

_____

6. What is the product of 91 and 15?

_____

7. Express $^{65}/_7$ as a mixed number.

_____

8. What is the 24th term given that the nth term of a sequence is as follows: $(n + 2n) - 8$?

_____

9. $a = 120°$. What is the value of c?

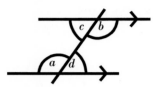

_____ °

10. The temperatures over 4 days were 27°C, 28°C, 33°C and 32°C. What was the mean temperature?

_____ °C

11. Express $^{11}/_{20}$ as a decimal.

_____

12. This clock is 20 minutes fast. What is the correct time? Give your answer in 12-hour clock format.

```
13 : 22
```

_____

13. A fair coin is thrown twice and lands on heads both times. What is the probability that the coin will land on tails with the next throw? Give your answer as a percentage.

_____ %

14. What is 70% of £110.00?

£ _____ . _____

15. Calculate $(35 + 65) + (1^2 - 1) × 5$?

_____

16. What is the number represented on this abacus in digits?

```
●●●        Th
●●●●●●     H
●●●●●      T
●●         U
```

_____

17. Rearrange $b = c + xd$ to make x the subject of the formula.

_____

18. The time now is 14:23. What will the time be $7\frac{1}{4}$ hours later? Give your answer in 24-hour clock format.

_____ : _____

19. This shape is made up of two equilateral triangles and a square. What is the value of x?

_____ °

20. Calculate the fifth prime number multiplied by the third square number.

_____

21. Damian takes 17 minutes to read 15 pages of a book. Given that he takes 187 minutes to complete the book at the same speed, how many pages are there?

_____

22. What is the exterior angle of a regular polygon with four sides?

_____ °

23. Which of the points on the diagram below shows the correct position of point A after it has been reflected in the dotted line?

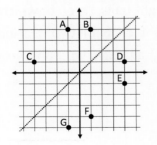

_____

24. Which of these nets will fold into the 3D shape below?

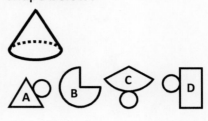

_____

25. What is the largest multiple of 70 that is less than 600?

_____

26. What is the remainder of $354 \div 6$?

_____

27. A cuboid is made up of three smaller cubes that have a volume of $27cm^3$ each. What is the surface area of the cuboid?

_____ cm^2

28. The radius of each circle inside the rectangle is 10mm. What is the perimeter of the rectangle?

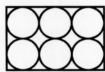

_____ mm

29. How many right angles are there in a turn from east to west?

_____

30. What is the perimeter of this equilateral triangle?

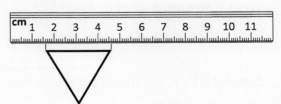

_____ cm

FIRST PAST THE POST

Test 8

Total
/30

1. Fill in the space below so that the pattern stays the same.

| 5 | 3 | 8 | 11 | | 30 |

2. On one Sunday the ratio of the time Tiana slept to the time she awoke was 1:3. For how many hours did she sleep?

_____ hr

3. Round 9873 to the nearest 100.

_____

4. $5 = 67 + x$. What is the value of x?

_____

5. What is the volume of this cube?

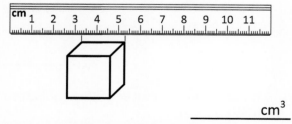

_____ cm^3

6. What is the product of 6, 7 and 11?

_____

7. Calculate $^2/_5 + {}^9/_{10}$. Give your answer as an improper fraction.

_____

8. A toy costs £1.40. How many toys can you buy with £10.00?

_____

9. What is the value of x?

_____

10. The rainfalls over 4 days were 1.6mm, 1.8mm, 2.2mm and 0.4mm. What was the mean rainfall?

_____ mm

11. What must 741 be divided by to get 0.0741?

_____

12. Mark buys five books which cost £7.50 each with a £50 note. How much change should he receive?

£ _____ .

13. Express $^{32}/_{40}$ as a percentage.

_____ %

14. What is the value of x?

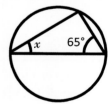

_____ °

15. A bag contains eight balls, three of which are red. What is the probability of picking a red ball from the bag? Give your answer as a fraction.

_____

16. $9x - 7 = 56$. What is the value of x?

_____

17. How many pairs of parallel faces does this shape have?

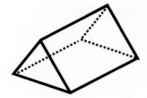

_____

18. What number is 98 less than 123?

_____

19. What is the sum of the fifth cube number and the tenth square number?

_____

20. Which of the points on the diagram below shows the correct position of point A after it has been reflected in the dotted line?

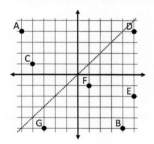

_____

21. A vertex of a regular polygon has an exterior angle of 45°. How many sides does the polygon have?

_____

22. Look at the bus timetable below. How long does it take to get from Hendon to Watford?

	Times
Hendon	12:30
Stanmore	13:12
Watford	13:57

_____ min

23. Express $^{1}/_{8}$ as a decimal.

_____

24. What is the lowest common multiple (LCM) of 5, 6 and 9?

_____

25. The area of square ABCD is 36cm^2. Given that the area of the shaded region is 18cm^2, what is the perimeter of the shaded region?

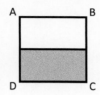

_____ cm

26. How many sides does a decagon have?

_____

27. What is the 20th term given that the nth term of a sequence is as follows: $1000 + 100n$?

_____

28. The angles of a triangle are in the ratio 2:1:1. What is the largest angle?

_____ °

29. How many lines of symmetry does this shape have?

_____

30. Kate and Tami win a jackpot of £100,000 and decide to split it so that Kate gets £40,000 more than Tami. How much does Tami get?

£ _____ . ____

FIRST PAST THE POST

Test 9

Total
/30

1. Calculate 75 + 675.

_____

2. Andy and Tom share 20 sweets in the ratio 7:3 respectively. How many more sweets does Andy receive than Tom?

_____

3. Round 4563 to the nearest 10.

_____

4. Calculate $^2/_5 \div {}^5/_8$.

_____

5. Fill in the spaces below so that the pattern stays the same.

	16	25	36	49	

6. Harry's allowance is £12 per week. Given that he saves half of his allowance every week, how many weeks does it take him to save £150?

_____

7. Calculate $^5/_8 + {}^1/_4$.

_____

8. Calculate 456 - 73.

_____

9. Reyvanth is facing southeast. In which direction will he be facing after turning 180°?

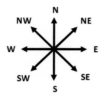

_____

10. What is the range of the following set of numbers: 90, 76, 99, 78, 88, 79, 77, 93?

_____

11. Calculate $5 \, ^3/_4 - {}^{18}/_4$.

_____

12. Look at the diagram below. How much do two pears weigh?

_____ kg

13. A chair costing £20.00 is increased in price by 25%. How much does it cost now?

£ _____ .

14. Calculate (14 - 7) × (2 + 10).

_____

15. What is the probability of an event that has an even chance of happening? Give your answer as a decimal.

_____

16. Simplify $7x + 2y - 8z - 3x + 8y + z$.

_____

17. This cylinder has a volume of 900m³. What is the area of one of its circular faces?

12m

_____ m²

18. How many pairs of parallel edges does a square pyramid have?

_____

19. What is the ratio between the numbers of lines of symmetry of an equilateral triangle to an isosceles triangle?

_____ :

20. This shape is made up of two isosceles triangles and a square. What is the perimeter of the shape?

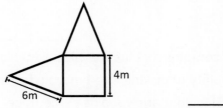

4m
6m

_____ m

21. What are the prime factors of 70?

_____

22. An interior angle of a regular polygon has a supplementary angle of 120°. What is the sum of its interior angles?

_____ °

23. How many rhombi can fit into a regular hexagon if the shapes have sides of the same length?

_____

24. The time now is 07:33. What time was it 2 ½ hours ago? Give your answer in 24-hour clock format.

_____ :

25. Express 0.78 as a fraction.

_____

26. How many lines of symmetry does this shape have?

_____

27. What are the coordinates of point B (5, 3) after a translation of three units to the right?

(_____ , _____)

28. What are the two cube numbers that have a sum of 91?

_____

29. The table below shows the possible totals for two fair dice thrown. What is the probability of throwing a total of 4 or 5? Give your answer as a fraction.

		Dice 1					
	+	1	2	3	4	5	6
	1	2	3	4	5	6	7
	2	3	4	5	6	7	8
Dice 2	3	4	5	6	7	8	9
	4	5	6	7	8	9	10
	5	6	7	8	9	10	11
	6	7	8	9	10	11	12

_____

30. How many pairs of perpendicular faces does a cube have?

_____

FIRST PAST THE POST

Test 10

Total
/30

1. What must be added to 6 to make 35?

_____

2. Round 99,763 to the nearest thousand.

_____

3. Juice is made by mixing water and squash in the ratio 9:2 respectively. How much water is in 22 litres of juice?

_____ l

4. Which of these is an obtuse angle?

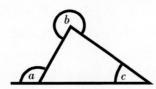

_____ °

5. Calculate 983 - 324.

_____

6. How many times greater is 117 than 13?

_____

7. Simplify $^{144}/_{300}$.

_____

8. Fill in the spaces below so that the pattern stays the same.

128		152	164	176		200

9. A box holds eight bottles of water. How many boxes are needed to store 59 bottles?

_____

10. This rectangular prism has a volume of 560cm³. What is the value of $x$cm?

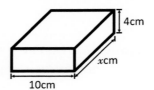

_____ cm

11. What is 20% of £180.00?

£ _____ . _____

12. A number machine has an output of 138 and an operation of '+ 67'. What is the input?

_____

13. A bag contains six blue marbles. What is the probability of picking a <u>red</u> marble from the bag? Give your answer as a percentage.

_____ %

14. $3x - 5 = -8x + 50$. What is the value of x?

_____

15. What is the number shown by the arrow in digits?

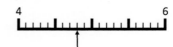

_____

16. The height from the base to the centre of this regular pentagon is 4cm. What is the area of the pentagon?

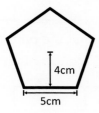

4cm

5cm

_____ cm²

17. What is the difference between the eighth prime number and the third cube number?

_____

18. What is the remainder of 567 ÷ 40?

_____

19. How many pairs of parallel edges does a cube have?

_____

20. A hexagonal prism has a length of 9cm and each hexagonal face has an area of 77cm². What is the volume of the prism?

_____ cm³

21. What is the order of rotational symmetry of this shape?

_____

22. Express 10.13pm in 24-hour clock format.

_____ :

23. Express 0.65 as a fraction.

_____

24. Calculate 93 ÷ 3 × (3 - 1).

_____

25. The ratio of three numbers that have a mean of 12 is 1:2:3. What is the largest number?

_____

26. What are the prime factors of 50?

_____

27. Look at the sign below. For how many hours is the office open per day?

| DAILY OFFICE HOURS |
| 9.00am to 1.00pm |
| 2.00pm to 5.30pm |

_____ hr

28. How many equilateral triangles can fit into a regular hexagon if the shapes have sides of the same length?

_____

29. Calculate 5 × 25 ÷ 5 + (78 - 25).

_____

30. What is the complementary angle of 67°?

_____ °

FIRST PAST THE POST

Test 11

Total
/30

1. What is the sum of 54 and 39?

   _____

2. Given that each digit can only be used once, what is the largest 5-digit number that can be made from the digits 5, 7, 3, 8 and 4?

   _____

3. What is the value of x?

   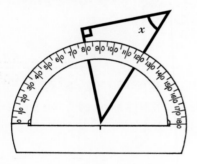

   _____ °

4. Calculate 78 ÷ 13.

   _____

5. Express $^{170}/_{200}$ as a percentage.

   _____ %

6. Seven children, each with 13 marbles, are playing marbles together. How many marbles do they have in total?

   _____

7. Four-sevenths of the 28 children in a playground are boys. How many girls are there?

   _____

8. Fill in the spaces below so that the pattern stays the same.

   | 5 | 10 | 15 | 20 | 25 | | |

9. $2x + 6y - 7z = w$. Given that $x = 3$, $y = 11$ and $z = 6$, what is the value of w?

   _____

10. Jim and Vanessa worked for 6 and 8 hours respectively at the same pay rate. Given that they were paid £98 between them, how much did Vanessa get paid?

    £_____ .

11. Calculate (4.38 - 0.98) × 2.

    _____

12. A number machine has an output of 90 and an operation of '× 15'. What is the input?

    _____

13. A bag contains eight black buttons. How many red buttons must be added so that there is an even chance of picking a black button?

    _____

14. What is the bearing of A from B?

    _____ °

15. How many tiles, measuring 6cm by 6cm by 0.5cm each, can fit into a box of volume of 216cm³?

    _____

16. What is the median of the following set of numbers: 19, 11, 12, 5, 8, 9, 9?

_____

17. Express $^{12}/_5$ as a decimal.

_____

18. This shape is made up of three identical isosceles triangles. What is the value of x?

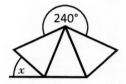

_____ °

19. The mean of three numbers is 7. Given that two of the numbers are 1 and 19, what is the other number?

_____

20. An interior angle of a regular polygon is 120°. How many sides does the polygon have?

_____

21. What is the order of rotational symmetry of this shape?

_____

22. Gemma is thinking of a cube number that is greater than 340, but less than 350. What is the number she is thinking of?

_____

23. What is the ratio of the lengths of the sides of an equilateral triangle in its simplest form?

_____ : _____

24. Express 17:08 in 12-hour clock format.

_____

25. Each small square of the diagram below has an area of 1cm². What is the area of the shape?

_____ cm²

26. Multiply the third cube number by the second square number.

_____

27. Which of the points on the diagram below shows the correct position of point A after it has been reflected in the dotted line?

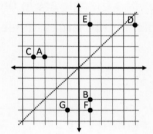

_____

28. What is the sum of the first three multiples of 7?

_____

29. The table below shows the number of biscuits eaten by Sam last week. What was the mean number of biscuits eaten last week?

Mon	Tues	Weds	Thurs	Fri	Sat	Sun
3	7	8	4	5	9	6

30. How many pairs of parallel faces does a pentagonal prism have?

_____

FIRST PAST THE POST

Test 12

Total
/30

1. What is the total number of dots?

_____

2. The interior angles of a triangle are in the ratio 1:2:2. How big are the largest angles?

_____ °

3. What is the value of the digit 6 in 6,231,522?

_____

4. Fill in the space below so that the pattern stays the same.

| 12 | 15 | 8 | 11 | 4 | 7 | |

5. Calculate 2^3 multiplied by 4^3.

_____

6. Calculate $^2/_3 + {}^7/_{10}$. Give your answer as an improper fraction.

_____

7. Nine oranges cost £1.80. What is the price of an orange?

£ _____ . _____

8. Jill is facing northwest. In which direction will she be facing after turning 270° clockwise?

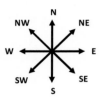

_____

9. What is the median of the following set of numbers: 3, 5, 6, 10, 8, 2?

_____

10. What is 0.059kg in grams?

_____ g

11. It is morning and this clock is 18 minutes behind. What is the correct time? Give your answer in 12-hour clock format.

_____

12. Express $^{17}/_{170}$ as a percentage.

_____ %

13. Calculate $(3^3 - 5 \times 5)^2$.

_____

14. One of the two circular faces of this cylinder has an area of 3.14cm^2. What is its volume?

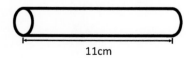

11cm

_____ cm^3

15. Calculate 18 × 16.

_____

16. A number is chosen at random from the single-digit numbers 0, 1, 2, 3, 4, 5, 6, 7, 8 and 9. Which of the arrows A, B, C or D shows the best position on the probability line for the event that the number chosen is prime?

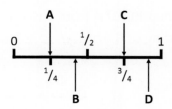

_____

17. How many vertices does a triangular pyramid have?

_____

18. $31x - 32 = -52x + 134$. What is the value of x?

_____

19. Calculate 890 - 123.

_____

20. Which of these is an acute triangle?

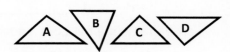

_____

21. The perimeter of a square is 28cm. What is its area?

_____ cm^2

22. How many tiles, measuring 40cm by 40cm each, would be needed to cover a wall of 1m by 800m?

_____

23. How many lines of symmetry does a regular heptagon have?

_____

24. Look at the bus timetable. How long does it take to get from South Harrow to North Harrow?

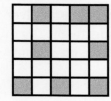

_____ min

25. What are the coordinates of point B (-2, 5) after a clockwise rotation of 90° about the origin?

(_____ , _____)

26. What is the sum of the interior angles of a hexagon?

_____ °

27. Express the shaded part of the grid as a decimal.

_____

28. Find the change from £5 after buying six birthday cards at 65p each.

£ _____ . _____

29. What is the product of 5 and 85?

_____

30. How many lines of symmetry does this shape have?

_____

Total
/30

1. Gemma has six 10p coins, two 2p coins, and seven 1p coins. How much money does she have in total?

£ _____ . _____

2. What is the value of the digit 4 in 653,643?

_____

3. A necklace is made out of gold and silver beads in the ratio 5:2 respectively. Given that there are 35 gold beads, how many silver beads are there?

_____

4. Which of these shapes represent a cross section of a sphere?

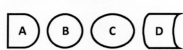

_____

5. A box of cream crackers contains 15 individual packs. Given that John buys 12 boxes, how many packs does he have in total?

_____

6. Express $6\frac{3}{8}$ as an improper fraction.

_____

7. What is the 112th term given that the nth term of a sequence is as follows: $n - 89$?

_____

8. How many quadrilaterals are there in the shape below?

_____

9. Given that the bearing of A from B is 120°, what is the bearing of B from A?

_____

10. The bag shown on the scales below contains 48 identical marbles. How much do 10 marbles weigh?

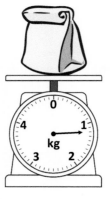

_____ kg

11. What is 90% of £330.00?

£ _____ . _____

12. What is the probability of a fair coin landing on tails twice in a row when it is tossed? Give your answer as a fraction.

_____

13. Rearrange $w = z - xy$ to make x the subject of the formula.

_____

14. A rectangular prism of volume 3200mm³ has a rectangular base of length 10mm and width 8mm. What is the height of the prism?

_____ mm

15. What is the perimeter of this shape?

_____ m

16. The time now is 06:43. What was the time 99 minutes ago? Give your answer in 24-hour clock format.

_____ : _____

17. Which three consecutive square numbers have a sum of 302?

_____

18. What is the order of rotational symmetry of a regular decagon?

_____

19. How many pairs of perpendicular sides does a regular quadrilateral have?

_____

20. Each small square of the diagram below has an area of 1cm². What is the area of the trapezium?

_____ cm²

21. The costs, in pence, of four chocolate bars are 50, 15, 45 and 19. What is the median cost?

_____ p

22. What is the scale factor of the enlargement of shape A to shape B, centred about the origin?

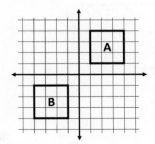

_____

23. How much greater is the total of £1.34 and £4.66, than the value of £12 divided by 5?

£ _____ . _____

24. How many 450ml bottles are needed to store 3 litres?

_____

25. The interior angles of a triangle are in the ratio 4:1:1. What is the supplementary angle of the largest angle?

_____ °

26. The bar graph below shows the number of items sold. How many more hamburgers were sold than hotdogs?

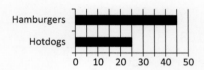

_____

27. Calculate $(35 \times 5 + 25) \div 2^3$.

_____

28. List the first three multiples of 17.

_____

29. Put the following set of numbers in order from the largest to smallest: 1.43, 1.34, 0.98, 0.93, 9.23, 1.14.

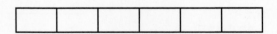

30. Tom had 57 Christmas cards. Given that he sent eight to people in his maths class and 14 to people in his English class, how many cards does he have left?

_____

Total
/30

1. 543 - x = 57. What is the value of x?

    _____

2. What is the value of the digit 5 in 12.053?

    _____

3. Calculate 168 ÷ 3.

    _____

4. A farmer divides up his land to grow
    potatoes, tomatoes and peppers in the ratio
    3:2:1 respectively. Given that the total area
    of the land is 192m^2, how much of it is used
    to grow tomatoes?

    _____ m^2

5. What is the third prime number multiplied
    by seven squared?

    _____

6. Calculate $^2/_{10}$ - $^2/_{15}$.

    _____

7. Fill in the spaces below so that the pattern
    stays the same.

    | 3 | 2 | 4 | 3 | 6 | | |

8. What is the value of x?

    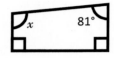

    _____ °

9. What is the range of the following set of
    numbers: 17, 78, 50, 45, 25?

    _____

10. Calculate ($^3/_{10}$ + $^2/_5$) ÷ 2.

    _____

11. What is the value of x?

    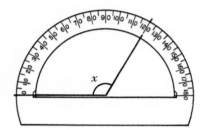

    _____ °

12. A CD costing £14.00 is increased in price by
    15%. How much does it cost now?

    £ _____ . _____

13. Express $^9/_{11}$ as a decimal to 3 decimal places.

    _____

14. What is the volume of this prism?

    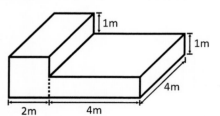

    _____ m^3

15. A letter is chosen at random from the 26 letters of the alphabet. Which of the arrows A, B, C or D shows the best position on the probability line for the event that the letter chosen is a vowel? (The letters a, e, i, o and u are vowels. All other letters are consonants.)

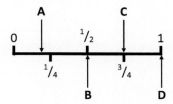

_____

16. How many faces does a cylinder have?

_____

17. Simplify $36x + 51y - 43z - 29x + 4y + 6z$.

_____

18. Subtract 56 from 234.

_____

19. How many tiles, measuring 3cm by 5cm each, are needed to cover a wall of 100cm by 45cm?

_____

20. How many lines of symmetry does a regular pentagon have?

_____

21. The time now is 16.49. What will the time be 4 ¼ hours later? Give your answer in 12-hour clock format.

_____

22. What is the order of rotational symmetry of this shape?

_____

23. What is the value of x?

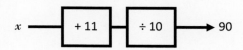

_____

24. What is the lowest common multiple (LCM) of the numbers four, six and eight?

_____

25. Multiply £4.49 by 6 and write the answer to the nearest £.

£ _____ . _____

26. Which of these is an acute angle?

_____

27. What is the sum of the interior angles of a regular polygon with seven sides?

_____ °

28. £22 is divided equally between seven people. How much is left?

_____ p

29. The bar graph below shows the number of items sold. How many more cupcakes were sold than chocolates?

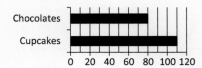

_____

30. What are the coordinates of point P (8, 22) after a reflection in the line $y = x$?

(_____ , _____)

Total
/30

1. Calculate 500 + 2 + 60 + 9000.

_____

2. A school has 1532 pupils. Round this number to the nearest 100.

_____

3. Ilesh and Ashley share £60 in the ratio 7:5 respectively. How much does Ilesh get?

£ _____ . _____

4. Write sixty-nine thousand, eight hundred and fifty-four in digits.

_____

5. The perimeter of the square is the same as that of the equilateral triangle. What is the length of one side of the square?

16cm

_____ cm

6. A supermarket orders 24 crates of soup. Given that each crate holds 270 cans of soup, how many cans of soup has the supermarket ordered?

_____

7. Calculate $^7/_{10}$ of $^5/_6$.

_____

8. What is the difference between the 4th and 6th terms in the following sequence: 4, 16, 6, 24, 14, …?

_____

9. The bearing of A from B is 90°. What is the bearing of B from A?

_____ °

10. What is the mean height of these buildings?

15m   105m   30m

_____ m

11. The ratio of boys to girls in a class is 4:5. Given that a teacher picks one student at random to answer a question, what is the probability of the student being a boy? Give your answer as a decimal to 3 decimal places.

_____

12. Express $^{120}/_{160}$ as a percentage.

_____ %

13. What is the area of this square?

cm 1 2 3 4 5 6 7 8 9 10 11

_____ cm^2

14. $10x + 25 = 100$. What is the value of x?

_____

15. What is the area of this parallelogram?

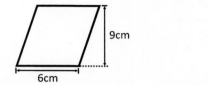

_____ cm^2

16. The time now is 16:36. What was the time $3\frac{1}{4}$ hours ago? Give your answer in 24-hour clock format.

_____ :

17. What is the seventh cube number subtracted from the tenth cube number?

_____

18. What is the order of rotational symmetry of a regular polygon with $n + 7$ sides? Give your answer in terms of n.

_____

19. List the first four multiples of 19.

_____

20. Each small square of the diagram below represents 1cm^2. What is the area of the triangle?

_____ cm^2

21. A number machine has an output of 57 and the operation '× 3'. What is the input?

_____

22. A polygon has n sides. What is the sum of its interior angles? Give your answer in terms of n.

_____

23. How many numbers from the following set of numbers are prime: 1, 43, 10, 24, 5, 3?

_____

24. The mean of a set of six numbers is 45. What is the new mean after 10 has been added to the set?

_____

25. What are the coordinates of point A (3, -2) after a translation of four units to the left and two units up?

(_____ , _____)

26. The table below shows the number of basketball matches won, drawn and lost by three teams. How many matches in total were won and drawn amongst the three teams?

	Team 1	Team 2	Team 3
Won	15	19	22
Drawn	4	5	0
Lost	6	1	3

_____

27. 23 pencils are taken out of a box of 112. How many are left in the box?

_____

28. Write down the number shown by the arrow.

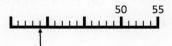

_____

29. By how many cm is a line of 23cm longer than another line of 6cm?

_____ cm

30. Mary has six bags of sweets. Given that each bag contains 39 sweets, how many sweets does she have in total?

_____

FIRST PAST THE POST

Test 16

Total
/30

1. Calculate the sum of 89 and 345.

    _____

2. What is 7°C above the temperature shown on this thermometer?

    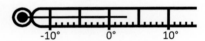

    _____ °C

3. Round 54 + 652 to the nearest 10.

    _____

4. Given that a track of 1200m is equally divided between eight runners, what is the distance that each runner has to cover?

    _____ m

5. Multiply the number of days in a week by the number of minutes in two hours.

    _____

6. How many thirds are there in two ones?

    _____

7. What is the sum of the 5th and 6th terms in the following sequence: 2, 2, 4, 8, 32, ...?

    _____

8. Mark is facing south. In which direction will he be facing after turning 270° clockwise and then 90° anticlockwise?

    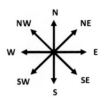

    _____

9. What is 55% of £240.00?

    £ _____ . _____

10. What is the ratio of six footballs to twelve hockey balls to eight tennis balls in its simplest form?

    _____ : _____ : _____

11. The table below shows the possible totals for two fair dice thrown. What is the probability of throwing a total of 7 or 11? Give your answer as a fraction.

    Dice 1

+	1	2	3	4	5	6
1	2	3	4	5	6	7
2	3	4	5	6	7	8
3	4	5	6	7	8	9
4	5	6	7	8	9	10
5	6	7	8	9	10	11
6	7	8	9	10	11	12

    Dice 2

    _____

12. How many edges does a pentagonal prism have?

    _____

13. $13x - 25 = -4x + 26$. What is the value of x?

    _____

14. The area of a face of a cube is 64cm^2. What is the volume of the cube?

    _____ cm^3

15. What is the difference between 54 and 89?

    _____

16. How many vertices does a pentagonal prism have?

_____

17. Express $^9/_5$ as a decimal?

_____

18. The shape below is made up of four identical rectangles. What is the area of one rectangle?

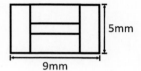

_____ mm^2

19. What are the coordinates of point P (-9, -7) after a translation of four units to the right and six units to the left?

(_____ , _____)

20. The time now is 11:51. What was the time 10 $^1/_2$ hours ago? Give your answer in 24-hour clock format.

_____ : _____

21. The circle below has a diameter of 10cm. What is the perimeter of the regular hexagon inside the circle?

_____ cm

22. What is the remainder of 930 ÷ 12?

_____

23. What is the product of the first three multiples of 3?

24. The table below shows the number of sweets eaten by Shaniqua last week. What was the mean number of sweets eaten?

Mon	Tues	Weds	Thurs	Fri	Sat	Sun
8	2	1	5	4	6	2

_____

25. Calculate $12 × 9 ÷ (3 ÷ 6)^2$.

_____

26. What is the next triangular number after 18?

_____

27. What is the difference between the number of lines of symmetry of an isosceles triangle, and the order of rotational symmetry of a square?

_____

28. Which of these triangles has the most lines of symmetry?

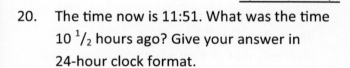

_____

29. Given that the means of numbers in sets A and B, each containing four numbers, are 8 and 12 respectively, what is mean of the numbers when both sets are combined?

_____

30. Shane has 13 boxes, each containing x chocolates, and two boxes, each containing y sweets. Write an expression which represents the total number of chocolates and sweets Shane has.

_____

Test 17

1. Simplify 7m + 9m + 13m - 14m.

_____ m

2. What is the value of the digit 6 in 356,920?

_____

3. There are 25 boys and 15 girls in a class. What is the ratio of boys to girls?

_____ : _____

4. What is the value of x?

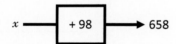

_____

5. Multiply the total number of wheels on two bicycles by the number of days in three weeks.

_____

6. How many halves are there in seven ones?

_____

7. How many dots should the next pattern have in the sequence below?

_____

8. What is the value of x?

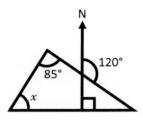

_____ °

9. It is afternoon and this clock is 80 minutes fast. What is the correct time? Give your answer in 12-hour clock format.

_____

10. A school bag costing £18.00 is reduced in price by 30%. How much does it cost now?

£ _____

11. In a bag there are six green balls, two red balls and a white ball. Without returning the ball after each choice, what is the highest probability of picking a matching pair? Give your answer as a fraction.

_____

12. Simplify $6x + 2y - 14z - 8x + 5y + 7z$.

_____

13. How many of the following set of numbers are prime: 5, 29, 32, 47, 65?

_____

14. How many lines of symmetry does a semicircle have?

_____

15. What is the name of a regular polygon with four pairs of parallel sides?

_____

16. Look at the bus timetable below. How long does it take to get from Hatfield to Golders Green?

	Times
Hatfield	06:42
High Barnet	07:30
Golders Green	08:00

_____ min

17. How many faces does a heptagonal prism have?

_____

18. A pad of papers costing £5.00 is reduced in price by 15%. How much does it cost now?

£ _____ . _____

19. The time now is 03:57. What will the time be 45 minutes later? Give your answer in 24-hour clock format.

_____ : _____

20. The perimeter of this rhombus is 48mm. What is its area?

10mm

_____ mm^2

21. Square ABCD has the coordinates A (2, 9), B (6, 9), C (6, 5) and D (x, y). What are the values of x and y?

$x =$ _____ , $y =$ _____

22. Given that each digit can only be used once, what is the smallest 5-digit number that can be made from the digits 1, 7, 5, 6 and 2?

_____

23. Express 0.78 as a fraction in its simplest form.

_____

24. What is the median of the following set of numbers: 10, 15, 40, 23, 50?

_____

25. Calculate (5 - 2) × 3^2 + 3.

_____

26. What is the value of x?

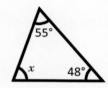
55°
x 48°

_____ °

27. Two-thirds of the 18 balls in a bag are red. How many balls in the bag are not red?

_____

28. Look at the pie chart below. Given that 360 items were sold altogether, how many more watches were sold than bracelets?

☐ watches ☐ bracelets

_____

29. List the next two multiples of 18 after 36.

_____

30. The cylinder below has a volume of 324cm^3. What is the area of one circular face?

9cm

_____ cm^2

FIRST PAST THE POST

Test 18

Total
/30

1. What is the perimeter of this square?

10m

_____ m

2. What number is 17 less than 89?

_____

3. What is the value of the digit 4 in 2134?

_____

4. Cement is made by mixing water and gravel in the ratio 3:8 respectively. How much gravel is needed make 209kg of cement?

_____ kg

5. A box of chocolate biscuits contains 12 individual packs. Given that Kara buys nine boxes, how many packs does she have in total?

_____

6. One-eighth of 32 pencils are metallic coloured. How many pencils are non-metallic coloured?

_____

7. Calculate 343 + 367.

_____

8. What is the 13th term given that the nth term of a sequence is as follows: $2n - 2$?

_____

9. Dave is facing east. In which direction will he be facing after turning 135° anticlockwise?

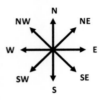

_____

10. A pencil set costing £16.00 is reduced in price by 10%. How much does it cost now?

_____

11. Calculate $(3 - (3 - 1))^3 + 1$.

_____

12. Look at the fair spinner below. What is the probability of the arrow landing on three? Give your answer as a fraction.

_____

13. How many vertices does a square pyramid have?

_____

14. What is the surface area of a cube with a volume of 125cm^3?

_____ cm^2

15. How many right-angled triangles, measuring 6cm by 5cm each, can you cut out from a rectangular cardboard of 35cm by 42cm?

_____

16. What is the mean of the following set of numbers: 5, 4, 8, 3, 5?

_____

17. Kyle has seven boxes, each containing x blue counters, and nine boxes, each containing y red counters. Write an expression which represents the total number of counters Kyle has.

_____

18. Calculate 324 - 213.

_____

19. What is the order of rotational symmetry of this shape?

_____

20. Express 0.896 as a fraction in its simplest form.

_____

21. What are the prime factors of 45?

_____

22. How many times does 25 go into 500?

_____

23. All the water in this measuring cup is poured equally into eight cups. How much water does each cup contain?

_____ l

24. What is the product of 10, 11 and 12?

_____

25. How many of the following set of numbers are even: 2, 12, 9, 73, 345, 120?

_____

26. Which of these is an obtuse triangle?

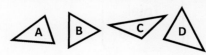

_____

27. An octagonal prism has a length of 11cm. Given that the sum of the areas of the two octagonal faces is 86cm^2, what is the volume of the prism?

_____ cm^3

28. What are the coordinates of point P (-2, 3) after a reflection in the y-axis followed by a translation of four units to the left?

(___ , ___)

29. The pie chart below shows which subjects were studied at A Level by 105 pupils. How many pupils chose to study art?

☐ art   ☐ other

_____

30. Express 2.22am in 24-hour clock format.

_____ :

FIRST PAST THE POST

Test 19

Total
/30

1. $a + b = 75$. Given that a is double b, what is the value of a?

_____

2. Round 948.543 to the nearest 100.

_____

3. Subtract 34 from 523.

_____

4. How many triangles are there in this shape?

_____

5. What is the product of 3, 19 and 2?

_____

6. How many sixths are there in two-thirds?

_____

7. What is the 15th term given that the nth term of a sequence is as follows: $n^2 - n$?

_____

8. Which of these is a reflex angle?

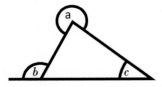

_____

9. What is the mode of the following set of numbers: 35, 33, 23, 33, 34, 25, 53?

_____

10. Express $^{49}/_{70}$ as a percentage.

_____ %

11. Calculate $(2^2)^2 + (60 + 40)^2$.

_____

12. In a drawer there are 20 white socks and 16 green socks. How many socks must you take out of the drawer before you are certain to have a matching pair?

_____

13. Two tennis players each have a ratio of good serves to bad serves. Given that Sam and Ben have ratios of 4:13 and 9:25 respectively, who is more likely to make a good serve?

_____

14. Look at the fair spinner below. What is the probability of the arrow landing on five? Give your answer as a fraction.

_____

15. Calculate $(5^2 + 35) \div 5 - 10$.

_____

16. 350ml of water is added to the measuring jug below. How much water does it contain now?

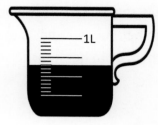

_____ ml

17. What is the volume of a cube with a surface area of 54cm²?

_____ cm³

18. $9x + 3y - 6z = w$. Given that $x = 12$, $y = 1$ and $z = 8$, what is the value of w?

_____

19. Calculate 123 + 429.

_____

20. What is the order of rotational symmetry of this shape?

_____

21. How many squares with 3cm sides can you cut out from a rectangular piece of cardboard of 1.5m by 2.1m?

_____

22. Express 23:27 in 12-hour clock format.

_____

23. Look at parallelogram ABCD below. Given that angle ADC is 62°, what is the angle BAD?

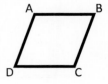

_____ °

24. How many times does 13 go into 221?

_____

25. Hiren buys five bags of crisps at 59p each. How much does he pay?

£ _____ .

26. Raven's call lasts for 15 minutes. Given that he is charged at 16p per minute, how much does the call cost him?

£ _____ .

27. What is the surface area of this triangular prism?

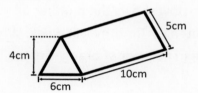

_____ cm²

28. What is the lowest common multiple (LCM) of the numbers 8, 4 and 7?

_____

29. Look at the price chart below. What is the total cost of sending two small letters, two large letters, a small parcel and two large parcels?

	Letter	Parcel
Small	£0.90	£3.40
Large	£1.50	£5.00

£ _____ .

30. Find three consecutive positive even integers such that three times the second integer equals four more than the sum of the first and third integers.

_____

Test 20

Total
/30

1. Calculate 270° + 676°.

    _____ °

2. The table below shows the number of oranges eaten by Timothy last week. What is the median number of oranges eaten last week?

Mon	Tues	Weds	Thurs	Fri	Sat	Sun
9	2	5	6	8	10	11

    _____

3. Calculate $6 + (65 \div 5)^2$.

    _____

4. What is the value of x?

    200 —— $+ x$ —— $\div 10$ —— 25

    _____

5. Calculate 68 multiplied by 50.

    _____

6. Express $^{219}/_7$ as a mixed number.

    _____

7. Three-fifths of 35 doughnuts are chocolate doughnuts and the rest are jam doughnuts. How many jam doughnuts are there?

    _____

8. What is the 7th term in the following sequence: 0, 1, 1, 2, 3, …?

    _____

9. The diagram below shows the direction of Nita's school from her house. What is the bearing of her school from her house?

    _____ °

10. What is the range of the following set of weights: 55kg, 45kg, 60kg, 64kg, 42kg?

    _____ kg

11. What is the value of x?

    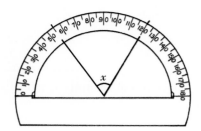

    _____ °

12. What is 20% of £440.00?

    £ _____ .

13. The ratio of boys to girls in a class of 32 pupils is 3:5. How many girls are there?

    _____

14. This cuboid is made up of smaller cubes of volume 1cm³. What is the volume of the cuboid?

    _____ cm³

15. What is the probability of picking a king from a complete deck of 52 cards? Give your answer as a fraction.

_____

16. The height from the base to the centre of the regular hexagon is shown below. What is the area of the hexagon?

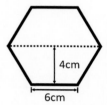

_____ cm²

17. Which of the following numbers is both a triangular and a square number: 25, 15, 16, 4, 36, 64, 8?

_____

18. Calculate 879 - 539.

_____

19. How many tiles, measuring 6cm by 6cm each, would be needed to cover a wall of 180cm by 40cm?

_____

20. Which of these is a right-angled triangle?

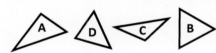

_____

21. Six equilateral triangles with 12cm sides are arranged to make a regular hexagon. What is the perimeter of the hexagon?

_____ cm

22. The time now is 19:44. What will the time be 26 minutes later? Give your answer in 24-hour clock format.

_____ :

23. Which of these shapes have rotational symmetry of order one?

_____

24. What are the coordinates of the centre of circle C (-4, 8) after a translation of seven units to the right and six units down.

_____(___ , ___)

25. Express 0.45 as a fraction in its simplest form.

_____

26. Fill in the space below so that the pattern stays the same.

	20	10	16	8	14

27. How many faces does a triangular prism have?

_____

28. Rearrange $p = q + rt$ to make r the subject of the formula.

_____

29. What is the value of the digit 5 in 533,620?

_____

30. The shape below is made up of four identical rectangles. What is the total area of the shape?

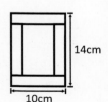

_____ mm²

BLANK PAGE

Your Handy Glossary

Learn the meanings of the terms listed below to expand your mathematical vocabulary.

Apothem - a line segment from the centre of a regular polygon to the midpoint of one of its sides.

Bearing - an angle given in three figures that is measured clockwise from the north direction, e.g. 025°.

BIDMAS - an acronym for Brackets, Indices, Division and Multiplication, and Addition and Subtraction. It is the agreed order of operations used to clarify which should be performed first in a given expression.

Bimodal - when a collection of data has two modes, e.g. if the dataset is: {1, 1, 1, 2, 4, 5, 5, 5}, the two modes are 1 and 5.

Bisect - to divide into two equal parts.

Coefficient - a constant that is placed before a variable in an algebraic expression, e.g. in the term $4x$, the coefficient is 4.

Complementary angles - two angles are complementary if they add up to 90°.

Cube number - a number produced when a digit is multiplied by itself twice, e.g. 1, 8, 27, 64.

Edge - a line segment that joins two vertices of a 2D shape, or a line segment at which two faces meet in a 3D shape.

Enlargement - a type of transformation in which the size of an object is changed whilst the ratio of the lengths of its sides stays the same.

Equidistant - the same distance from a common point.

Face - an individual surface of a 3D shape.

Fair - a fair item or event is free from bias.

Gallon - a unit of volume used for measuring liquids, equal to 8 pints or 4.55 litres.

Gradient - a gradient is a measure of the steepness of a straight line.

Highest common factor (HCF) - the largest number that is a factor of two or more given numbers, e.g. 5 is the highest common factor of 10 and 15.

Imperial units - the system of units first defined in the British Weights and Measures Act, e.g. 3 feet.

Inscribe - to draw a shape within another so that their boundaries touch but do not intersect.

Integer - a whole number, i.e. not a decimal or a fraction.

Isosceles trapezium - a trapezium which has one line of symmetry, two pairs of equal angles and one pair of parallel sides.

Leap year - a calendar year occurring every four years, totalling 366 days and including the 29th February, e.g. the year 2012 was a leap year.

Lowest common multiple (LCM) - the smallest number that is a multiple of two or more given numbers, e.g. 6 is the lowest common multiple of 2 and 3.

Metric units - The system of units based on multiples of 10, e.g. millimetre (mm), centimetre (cm) or metre (m).

Net - a 2D pattern that can be cut out and folded to make a 3D shape.

Parallel - lines that run side-by-side, always the same distance apart and never crossing, even if they are extended.

Perimeter - the total distance around the outside of a 2D shape.

Perpendicular - two lines are perpendicular if they intersect at an angle of 90° to each other.

Polygon - a 2D shape with three or more straight sides and no curved sides, e.g. triangle, pentagon, hexagon.

Polyhedron - a 3D shape with polygonal faces, e.g. triangular pyramid or octahedron.

Prime factor - one of a collection of prime numbers whose product is a particular number, i.e. a factor that is also a prime number.

Prime number - an integer greater than 1 that has no whole factors other than 1 and itself, e.g. 2, 3, 5.

Prism - a solid 3D shape with two identical, parallel end faces that are connected by flat sides.

Pyramid - a solid 3D shape whose base is a polygon and which has triangular faces that meet at the top at a single vertex, e.g. square pyramid.

Quadrilateral - a 2D shape with four straight sides. Quadrilaterals are polygons.

Reflective symmetry - a shape or an object has reflective symmetry if an imaginary line can be drawn that divides the shape into two, so that one half is a reflection of the other.

Regular - a regular polygon has sides of equal length.

Remainder - a number that is left over after division.

Rotational symmetry - a shape or an object has rotational symmetry if it can be rotated but still seems to have the same original position.

Scalene - a scalene triangle has sides of unequal lengths.

Sequence - a list of numbers or objects in a particular order defined by a specific pattern.

Square number - a number produced when a digit is multiplied by itself once, e.g. 1, 4, 9 or 16.

Supplementary angles - two angles are supplementary if they add up to 180°.

Triangle - a 2D shape with three straight sides. Triangles are polygons.

Triangular number - a figurate number that can be represented by a regular triangular arrangement of equally spaced points, e.g. 1, 3, 6: • ∴ ∷

Vertex - a point at which two or more straight lines meet.

Place Value

The numerical value of a digit in a number. For example, in the number 1234.567, the digit 3 has a place value of tens.

1	2	3	4	.	5	6	7
thousands	hundreds	tens	units	decimal point	tenths	hundredths	thousandths

Special Numbers

	1st	2nd	3rd	4th	5th	6th	7th	8th	9th	10th	11th	12th	13th	14th	15th	16th	17th	18th	19th	20th
Even	2	4	6	8	10	12	14	16	18	20	22	24	26	28	30	32	34	36	38	40
Odd	1	3	5	7	9	11	13	15	17	19	21	23	25	27	29	31	33	35	37	39
Square	1	4	9	16	25	36	49	64	81	100	121	144	169	196	225	256	289	324	361	400
Cube	1	8	27	64	125	216	343	512	729	1000	1331	1728	2197	2744	3375	4096	4913	5832	6859	8000
Triangular	1	3	6	10	15	21	28	36	45	55	66	78	91	105	120	136	153	171	190	210
Prime	2	3	5	7	11	13	17	19	23	29	31	37	41	43	47	53	59	61	67	71
Fibonacci	1	1	2	3	5	8	13	21	34	55	89	144	233	377	610	987	1597	2584	4181	6765

Equivalent Decimals, Fractions & Percentages

Percentage	5%	10%	15%	20%	25%	30%	35%	40%	45%	50%	55%	60%	65%	70%	75%	80%	85%	90%	95%	100%	150%
Fraction	$\frac{1}{20}$	$\frac{1}{10}$	$\frac{3}{20}$	$\frac{1}{5}$	$\frac{1}{4}$	$\frac{3}{10}$	$\frac{7}{20}$	$\frac{2}{5}$	$\frac{9}{20}$	$\frac{1}{2}$	$\frac{11}{20}$	$\frac{3}{5}$	$\frac{13}{20}$	$\frac{7}{10}$	$\frac{3}{4}$	$\frac{4}{5}$	$\frac{17}{20}$	$\frac{9}{10}$	$\frac{19}{20}$	$\frac{1}{1}$	$\frac{3}{2}$
Decimal	0.05	0.1	0.15	0.2	0.25	0.3	0.35	0.4	0.45	0.5	0.55	0.6	0.65	0.7	0.75	0.8	0.85	0.9	0.95	1	1.5

Mathematical Symbols

+	addition sign
−	subtraction sign
×	multiplication sign
÷	division sign
±	positive or negative
=	equals sign
<	less than
>	greater than
≈	approximately equal to
≤	less than or equal to
≥	greater than or equal to
≠	not equal to
a^2	squared number
a^3	cubed number
%	per cent
$\sqrt{a}$	square root
$\sqrt[3]{a}$	cubed root
$\dot{a}$	recurring number
$a : b$	ratio
$a°$	degrees
$\bar{a}$	mean
(x, y)	coordinates
⌐	right angle
$\binom{x}{y}$	column vector (column matrix)
$^a/_b$	fraction
$\{a, b\}$	dataset
π	pi

Equivalent Periods of Time

1 minute	60 seconds
1 hour	60 minutes
1 day	24 hours
1 week	7 days
1 year	12 months (365 days)
1 leap year	366 days
1 decade	10 years
1 century	100 years
1 millennium	1,000 years

Roman Numerals

When a symbol appears after a numerically larger number, it is added, but if the symbol appears before a numerically larger number, it is subtracted.

1	I	40	XL
2	II	50	L
3	III	60	LX
4	IV	70	LXX
5	V	80	LXXX
6	VI	90	XC
7	VII	100	C
8	VIII	200	CC
9	IX	300	CCC
10	X	400	CD
20	XX	500	D
30	XXX	1,000	M

Time Conversion

24-hour clock	12-hour clock
00:00	12.00am
01:00	1.00am
02:00	2.00am
03:00	3.00am
04:00	4.00am
05:00	5.00am
06:00	6.00am
07:00	7.00am
08:00	8.00am
09:00	9.00am
10:00	10.00am
11:00	11.00am
12:00	12.00pm
13:00	1.00pm
14:00	2.00pm
15:00	3.00pm
16:00	4.00pm
17:00	5.00pm
18:00	6.00pm
19:00	7.00pm
20:00	8.00pm
21:00	9.00pm
22:00	10.00pm
23:00	11.00pm

Units of Measurement

Metric system			Imperial system		
	Units	Conversion	Units	Conversion	Metric approximation
Mass	milligram (mg)	1mg = 0.1cg = 0.001g	ounce (oz)	1oz = $\frac{1}{16}$ lb	1oz ≈ 28g
	centigram (cg)	1cg = 10mg = 0.01g	pound (lb)	1lb = 16oz	1lb ≈ 0.45kg
	gram (g)	1g = 100cg = 0.001kg	stone (st)	1st = 14lb	1st ≈ 6kg
	kilogram (kg)	1kg = 1000g = 0.001t	ton	1 ton = 160st	1 ton ≈ 0.91 tonne
	tonne (t)	1t = 1,000,000g = 1000kg			
Length	millimetre (mm)	1mm = 0.1cm = 0.001m	inch (in or ")	1in = $\frac{1}{12}$ ft	1in ≈ 25mm
	centimetre (cm)	1cm = 10mm = 0.01m	foot (ft or ')	1ft = 12in	1ft ≈ 30cm
	metre (m)	1m = 100cm = 0.001km	yard (yd)	1yd = 3ft	1yd ≈ 91cm
	kilometre (km)	1km = 100,000cm = 1000m	mile	1 mile = 1760yd	1 mile ≈ 1.6km
Volume	millilitre (ml)	1ml = 0.1cl = 0.001l = 1cm³	fluid ounce (fl. oz)	1fl. oz = $\frac{1}{20}$ pt	1fl. oz ≈ 28ml
	centilitre (cl)	1cl = 10ml = 0.01l = 10cm³	pint (pt)	1pt = 20fl. Oz	1pt ≈ 0.57l
	litre (l)	1l = 100cl = 0.001kl = 1000cm³	gallon (gal)	1gal = 8pt	1gal ≈ 4.5l
	kilolitre (kl)	1kl = 1000l = 1,000,000cm³			

Types of Angles

Zero angle:
Equivalent to 0°.

The angle AÔB is an example of a zero angle.

Acute angle:
An angle smaller than 90°, but greater than 0°.

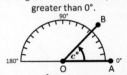

Angle *c*° (AÔB) is an example of an acute angle.

Right angle:
An angle of 90°.

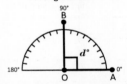

Angle *d*° (AÔB) is an example of a right angle.

Obtuse angle:
An angle between 90° and 180°.

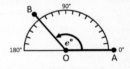

Angle *e*° (AÔB) is an example of an obtuse angle.

Flat angle:
The angle formed on a straight line, equal to 180°

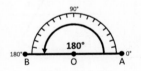

The angle AÔB is an example of a flat angle.

Reflex angle:
An angle above 180° but below 360°.

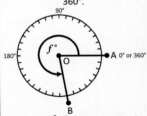

Angle *f*° (AÔB) is an example of a reflex angle.

Full rotation:
A full turn equal to 360°.

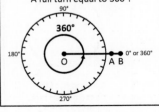

Pairs of Angles

Alternate angles:
The angles on opposite sides of a transversal between two parallel lines.

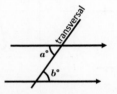

Alternate angles are always equal; i.e. *a*° = *b*°.

Complementary angles:
Two angles that add up to 90°.

Since *a*° + *b*° = 90°, they are complementary.

Supplementary angles:
Any two angles that have a sum of 180°.

The two angles *a*° and *b*° are supplementary.

Vertically opposite angles:
Equal angles that are opposite each other when two lines are crossed.

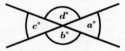

a° = *c*° and *b*° = *d*°; i.e. vertically opposite angles are always equal.

Corresponding angles:
The angles which are identical to each other between a transversal and parallel lines.

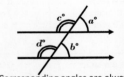

Corresponding angles are always equal; i.e. *a*° = *b*° and *c*° = *d*°.

Angles in a revolution:
The angles formed when lines intersect each other at a point.

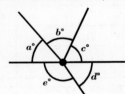

a° + *b*° + *c*° + *d*° + *e*° = 360°; i.e. angles in a revolution always add up to 360°.

2D Shapes

Figures with two dimensions: length and width, but no depth.

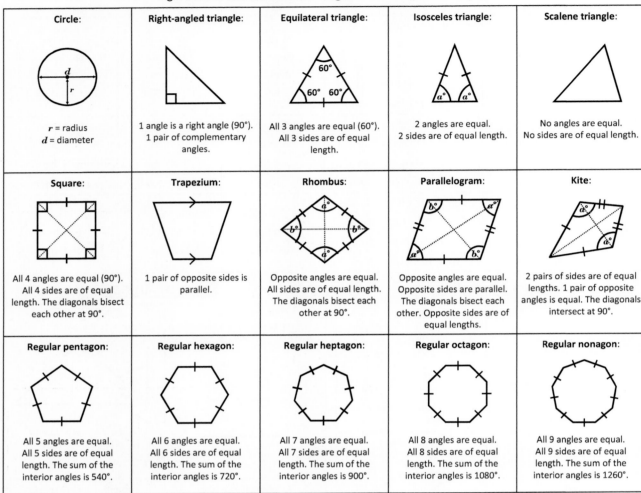

Circle:	Right-angled triangle:	Equilateral triangle:	Isosceles triangle:	Scalene triangle:
r = radius d = diameter	1 angle is a right angle (90°). 1 pair of complementary angles.	All 3 angles are equal (60°). All 3 sides are of equal length.	2 angles are equal. 2 sides are of equal length.	No angles are equal. No sides are of equal length.
Square:	**Trapezium:**	**Rhombus:**	**Parallelogram:**	**Kite:**
All 4 angles are equal (90°). All 4 sides are of equal length. The diagonals bisect each other at 90°.	1 pair of opposite sides is parallel.	Opposite angles are equal. All sides are of equal length. The diagonals bisect each other at 90°.	Opposite angles are equal. Opposite sides are parallel. The diagonals bisect each other. Opposite sides are of equal lengths.	2 pairs of sides are of equal lengths. 1 pair of opposite angles is equal. The diagonals intersect at 90°.
Regular pentagon:	**Regular hexagon:**	**Regular heptagon:**	**Regular octagon:**	**Regular nonagon:**
All 5 angles are equal. All 5 sides are of equal length. The sum of the interior angles is 540°.	All 6 angles are equal. All 6 sides are of equal length. The sum of the interior angles is 720°.	All 7 angles are equal. All 7 sides are of equal length. The sum of the interior angles is 900°.	All 8 angles are equal. All 8 sides are of equal length. The sum of the interior angles is 1080°.	All 9 angles are equal. All 9 sides are of equal length. The sum of the interior angles is 1260°.

3D Shapes

Figures with three dimensions: length, width and height.

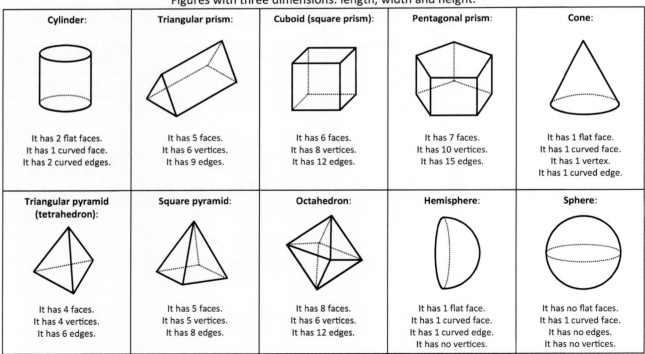

Cylinder:	Triangular prism:	Cuboid (square prism):	Pentagonal prism:	Cone:
It has 2 flat faces. It has 1 curved face. It has 2 curved edges.	It has 5 faces. It has 6 vertices. It has 9 edges.	It has 6 faces. It has 8 vertices. It has 12 edges.	It has 7 faces. It has 10 vertices. It has 15 edges.	It has 1 flat face. It has 1 curved face. It has 1 vertex. It has 1 curved edge.
Triangular pyramid (tetrahedron):	**Square pyramid:**	**Octahedron:**	**Hemisphere:**	**Sphere:**
It has 4 faces. It has 4 vertices. It has 6 edges.	It has 5 faces. It has 5 vertices. It has 8 edges.	It has 8 faces. It has 6 vertices. It has 12 edges.	It has 1 flat face. It has 1 curved face. It has 1 curved edge. It has no vertices.	It has no flat faces. It has 1 curved face. It has no edges. It has no vertices.

Area Formulae

Area of a regular polygon = $^{1}/_{2}$ × apothem × perimeter
= $^{1}/_{2} \times a \times p$

Area of a triangle = $^{1}/_{2}$ × base × perpendicular height
= $^{1}/_{2} \times b \times h$

Area of a circle = pi × radius²
= $\pi \times r^2$

Area of a parallelogram = base × perpendicular height
= $b \times h$

Area of a kite = $^{1}/_{2}$ × product of the two diagonals
= $^{1}/_{2} \times a \times b$

Area of a quadrilateral = length × width
= $l \times w$

Area of a rhombus = $^{1}/_{2}$ × product of the two diagonals
= $^{1}/_{2} \times a \times b$

Area of a trapezium = $^{1}/_{2}$ × sum of the lengths of the parallel sides × perpendicular height
= $^{1}/_{2} \times (a + b) \times h$

Volume Formulae

Volume of a cuboid = length × width × height
= $l \times w \times h$

Volume of a prism = area of cross-section × height
= $B \times h$

Other Useful Formulae

Surface area of a 3D shape = sum of the areas of all the faces

Perimeter of a shape = sum of the lengths of all the sides

Circumference of a circle = 2 × pi × radius
= $2 \times \pi \times r$

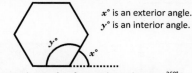

$x°$ is an exterior angle.
$y°$ is an interior angle.

An exterior angle of a regular polygon = $^{360°}/_{\text{number of sides}}$
= $^{360°}/_{n}$

An interior angle of a regular polygon = $^{180° \times (\text{number of sides - 2})}/_{\text{number of sides}}$
= $^{180° \times (n - 2)}/_{n}$

Probability

A measure of how likely it is for an event to occur.

The probability of event A happening is given by: P(A) = number of favourable outcomes ÷ total number of outcomes.

'And' rule:	'Or' rule:
The 'and' rule is used to find the probability of a combination of independent events.	The 'or' rule is used to find the probability of a combination of mutually exclusive events.
The probability of events A and B happening is: P(A and B) = P(A) × P(B)	The probability of event A or B happening is: P(A or B) = P(A) + P(B)
The word 'and' is replaced by a multiplication sign.	The word 'or' is replaced by an addition sign.

Tree diagram:

One way of illustrating probability of events is by using branches, e.g. a tree diagram illustrating two tosses of an unbiased coin.

```
              0.5    head
       head
      0.5    0.5    tail

      0.5    0.5    head
       tail
             0.5    tail
```

You can use the 'and' rule and 'or' rule with the tree diagram.
Simply multiply probabilities along the branches, and add probabilities down the columns.

Probability scale:

A scale, which goes from zero to one, measuring the likelihood of an outcome.

impossible   0.25   equally likely   0.75   certain

0   improbable   0.5   probable   1

Picking out a black marble from a bag which contains three blue marbles only.

There is an even chance of a fair coin landing on heads or tails.

Picking out a red marble from a bag which contains three red marbles.

Remember that probabilities can be expressed using fractions, decimals or percentages.

Venn diagram:

A diagram showing all logical relations for a collection of sets using overlapping circles, non-overlapping circles and a rectangular boundary.

Venn diagram showing the first ten positive integers.

Triangular number (Set **A**)   Odd number (Set **B**)

Each number represents an element of a set.

The circle represents a set. In this case, it is a set of odd numbers.

6
1
9
3
5
10
7
8
4   2

The rectangle represents the universal set; that is, all the elements.

Some useful Venn diagram patterns.

set **A**   set **B**   not **A**   not **B**

A or **B**   **A** and **B**   only **A** or only **B**   not **A** and not **B**